The Odyssey

Homer

Academic Industries, Inc.
West Haven, Connecticut 06516

ISBN 0-88301-756-3

Published by
Academic Industries, Inc.
The Academic Building
Saw Mill Road
West Haven, Connecticut 06516

Printed in the United States of America

about the author

Nearly thirty-two hundred years ago, long before the Greeks ever had a written language, Homer lived and told his stories. He was a bard—a wandering poet who kept his country's great legends alive by reciting them over and over.

Most people believe that Homer was blind. Perhaps he was able to compose and remember all his poems because he could see nothing to distract him from his thoughts. When he arrived at a village, or at the home of a wealthy man, all work stopped. A great feast was held, and everyone sat around afterward to listen to Homer's stories. The men and women, gods and goddesses he spoke about were part of Greece's legendary history. In their own way, his stories became one of the things that held this nation of city-states together.

Although Homer must have composed many poems during his lifetime, he is best known for the *Iliad,* his story of the Trojan War, and the *Odyssey,* the story of the wanderings of the hero Odysseus. Together, these two books are counted among the finest works ever composed by man.

The Odyssey

Homer

Telemachus

Penelope

Odysseus

Circe

Calypso

Zeus

Athena

Poseidon

More than 2,000 years ago, a great storyteller named Homer wandered from village to village in Greece. All that Homer owned were his harp and his clothes. But Homer was welcome everywhere.

Look, Father, it is Homer!

Call the people of our village. Today we shall hold a feast to honor our great guest.

So Homer began his story by calling on the gods.

Hear me, gods, in all your glory. Use my voice to tell your story!

The Greeks believed in many gods. The most powerful of them all was Zeus, the god of the sky. But it was Zeus' brother, Poseidon, who caused Odysseus to have so much trouble when he came home from the war. Poseidon was the god of the sea.

When Odysseus was on his way home, a great storm sank his ship. The last of his men were drowned. The sea carried Odysseus to the island of Ogygia, where a goddess named Calypso lived. Here Odysseus stayed for nearly ten years, unable to return home.

Poor Odysseus! For so long you have been sad. But why do you sit alone on the shore? Your ships and your men are gone forever.

Come, Odysseus. You must forget your wife and son. I will let you live forever if you will stay with me.

You are lovely, Calypso, but how can I forget the people who have not forgotten *me*?

From their home on Mount Olympus, the gods looked down on Odysseus and Calypso.

O Father Zeus, it is cruel of Calypso to force Odysseus to stay on her island.

No, dear Athena, it is Poseidon who keeps Odysseus from going home. Odysseus made Poseidon very angry by blinding his son, the Cyclops.

But just now Poseidon is visiting the land of Ethiopia. Perhaps we can help Odysseus.

O Father, please send someone to tell Calypso to let Odysseus go. I will go to Ithaca and tell Odysseus' son Telemachus to have hope. He lives in troubled times while he waits for the return of his father.

And so Athena, who was the goddess of wisdom, put on her golden sandals and went to earth. When she reached Ithaca, Athena changed herself to look like a man.

Soon she met Odysseus' son, Telemachus.

Welcome, stranger! We always honor travelers who are far from their homes.

Who are those drunken men who eat your food without a prayer to the gods or thanks to you?

You must be from far away if you do not know the sad story of this house.

They are evil men who come here day after day. They eat up my father's food. They also try to make my mother marry one of them, but she always refuses. My mother believes that my father will return. But even *I* fear that he is dead.

If I were the son of Odysseus, I would have a meeting in the village tomorrow. I would make these terrible things stop. Then I would sail to Pylos to see if there were any news about my father.

You see, I know Odysseus, and I believe that he will soon find a way to return.

And after saying these things, Athena left.

13

At this, Penelope left. Her son was no longer a child.

And as for you men, you may feast today, but tomorrow will be different. I will call a meeting in the village, and I will drive you out of my father's house!

The gods must have taken away your fear! But no god will make you king of Ithaca, even though that title should be yours.

We will see about that. Meanwhile, I will not allow you to eat my father's food or bother my mother.

And when morning came, Telemachus walked without fear to the meeting of the village.

15

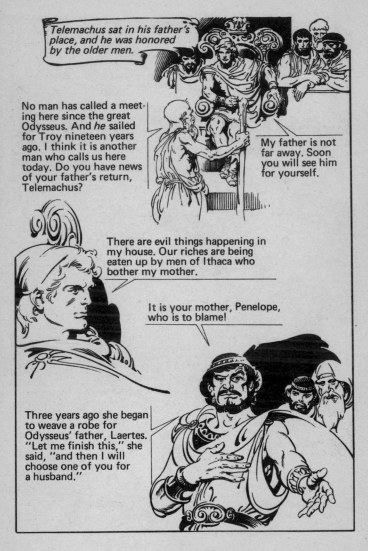

Telemachus sat in his father's place, and he was honored by the older men.

No man has called a meeting here since the great Odysseus. And *he* sailed for Troy nineteen years ago. I think it is another man who calls us here today. Do you have news of your father's return, Telemachus?

My father is not far away. Soon you will see him for yourself.

There are evil things happening in my house. Our riches are being eaten up by men of Ithaca who bother my mother.

It is your mother, Penelope, who is to blame!

Three years ago she began to weave a robe for Odysseus' father, Laertes. "Let me finish this," she said, "and then I will choose one of you for a husband."

16

But each night she pulls out the same work that she has done that day. And so the robe is still unfinished. It is *her* fault, I say. Make her choose, for she has treated us unfairly.

If you feel that she has been unfair, leave my house. Neither my mother nor I asked you to come, and we will thank Zeus when you are gone!

Suddenly, two eagles appeared in the sky. They fought, and one drove the other away.

It is a warning from Zeus. The fools who dishonor Odysseus will be killed!

Go home, old man, and tell your stories to your grandchildren. You think every bird in the sky is a sign of doom.

Let us not argue. The gods know what will happen. I will go to Pylos to find out about my father. If I learn that he is dead, my mother will choose one of you!

We'll send someone to follow him.

It is a trip from which he must not return!

But when Telemachus was ready, Athena caused the men to fall asleep, and Telemachus left safely.

Fear not, Mother. I shall return, and all will be well.

Meanwhile, Zeus had sent Hermes to help Odysseus.

My dear Calypso, Zeus knows that you love Odysseus. But you may not keep him with you any longer.

I have no ships or sailors, but if Zeus wants me to, I will help Odysseus leave.

So Calypso went to see Odysseus.

Weep no more, sad man. I would keep you with me always, but your heart is at home, and I cannot stop it. You may build a raft with this ax.

In four days Odysseus had built a raft.

A good breeze will carry you home safely. Goodbye, my love.

For eighteen days the breeze drove the raft westward.

I've made it! Surely the Phaiacians will help me home!

But Poseidon, who was returning from Ethiopia, saw the raft. He was still angry with Odysseus.

I know that Odysseus will return to his home. But first I will cause him to suffer a little more.

So Poseidon started a great storm.

Lucky were those who died at Troy! I must die in the sea alone!

The raft was smashed, but Athena sent the north wind to push Odysseus to shore.

Do not fear, Odysseus. Your luck will hold. It is the will of Zeus that you see your home again.

So Odysseus came at last to the shore of Scheria. He fell asleep under a wild olive tree that grew by a river.

Meanwhile, Athena went to the king's daughter Nausicaä and put a dream into her head. When she awoke, she went to her father.

Father, I've been told in a dream to take my maids and to go and wash our clothes in the river.

Not long afterward, Odysseus woke up to the sound of happy voices.

Do not be afraid. I am a poor traveler who has been cast up on your shore by a storm.

Stranger, you do not seem evil or foolish. All strangers and beggars come from Zeus, so we will help you.

Give the stranger food and clothing. Let him wash in the river.

When this was done, Nausicaä and her maids got ready to go back to their village.

You must go on alone, stranger. Go to my mother, the queen, and fall at her knees. If she likes you, my father will give you anything you want.

May Zeus bless you.

Then Athena covered Odysseus with an invisible fog so no one could see him until he reached the queen.

23

I beg you to help me. I have suffered so much! May the gods grant you joy if you help me to return to my home.

You shall have your wish, stranger. But now a feast is ready. You will be our guest.

As they ate, someone sang about the Trojan War. Tears filled Odysseus' eyes as he thought of his lost friends. King Alcinous saw this and spoke.

This song about Odysseus seems to trouble you. Tell us who you are, good stranger.

I am Odysseus, the son of Laertes.

You honor this home, for you are a great man! Please tell us your story.

Good king, you have shown me great kindness, and I will do as you ask. The name Odysseus is known by many. The story you will hear, no man has heard before.

Ten years ago we won the war against Troy. I left for home with twelve ships and the good men of Ithaca.

The trip home was not a happy one.

When we came to Ismaros, we attacked and burned the city. These people had been friendly with Troy. After this, I wanted to sail on, but the men begged to spend the night and have a feast on the beach.

During the night we were attacked by the Ciconians, who lived in a nearby village. Many men were killed before we could drive them away.

Next, a terrible storm came up that lasted nine days!

At last we came to an island. There were wild goats to eat, and we found a good spring for water. I decided to take some men and look around.

We had come to the island of the one-eyed giants called Cyclops. They were said to be a wild bunch, but we decided to go to a cave where one lived.

There we found some cheese that the giants had made from sheep's milk. My men wanted to take some and return quickly to the ships. But I wanted to stay and see the Cyclops who lived in the cave.

I told my men to hide, thinking that we could escape quietly later. But after the giant had driven his sheep into the cave, he rolled a huge stone in front of the door.

Zeus? I am stronger than Zeus!

I decided to speak to the Cyclops.

We are poor strangers. We ask you to treat us kindly, sir. After all, Zeus cares for the stranger.

The Cyclops reached down and grabbed two of my men. Then he ate them for supper.

Soon the Cyclops fell asleep. I had a plan.

We made a spear from a piece of firewood. While he was sleeping, we drove it into his eye and blinded him.

He shouted and roared, but he could not find us. When morning came, the sheep cried to go out. The Cyclops, of course, could not see, but he felt the sheep with his hands to keep us from getting out.

Then I had another plan. We tied three sheep together. Each of us got out by holding onto them underneath.

The Cyclops came to the shore as we sailed away. I called back to him.

If anyone should ask who put out your eye, tell him it was Odysseus of Ithaca!

Then the Cyclops cried out to Poseidon, the god of the sea.

Father Poseidon, grant me this wish! Curse Odysseus. Kill his men, sink his ships, and give him trouble when he comes to his home.

We sailed to the island of Aeolia where Aeolus, god of the winds, lived.

We spent a month on the island. When we left, good King Aeolus gave me a present. He put all the winds into a bag for me so they could not get out and cause us trouble. The west wind, however, he left out so it could carry us home.

I stayed awake during the whole trip so my men would not be tempted to open the bag. But, nearing Ithaca, I fell asleep. Then my sailors opened the bag.

The winds rushed out, and a great storm blew us far out to sea. On the seventh day of the storm, we came to an island. I didn't go too close in my ship, but the others sailed right into the harbor.

Suddenly the giant Laestrygonians appeared on the cliffs.

All the ships and men in the harbor were lost when the giants attacked. Only my ship and men got away. We sailed on, feeling very sad.

Soon we came to another island. We had no food, so Eurylochus took half the men to try to find some.

On the island they found the home of a goddess named Circe. She invited them into her house. Wise Eurylochus stayed behind to watch for a trick.

As Eurylochus looked on, Circe gave the men a drink that turned them into pigs! Frightened, Eurylochus ran back to the ship.

Eurylochus begged me to sail away, but I wanted to rescue my men. Just then I met the god Hermes. He gave a secret herb which would protect me from Circe's tricks.

Soon after, Circe tapped me with her wand. I stepped back and drew my sword.

You must be Odysseus. Hermes told me that my magic would not work on you. Come, put away your sword. Let us be friends.

I answered her angrily.

How can we be friends when you have turned my men into pigs?

Then I will turn them back into men. And I promise not to play any more tricks.

Circe did as she had said. Then she called her maids to prepare a great feast.

For a whole year we feasted to forget about what we had been through. And we decided to rest in case trouble lay ahead.

34

Finally I told Circe that we had to leave. Sadly she answered:

Oh, Odysseus! You have known what only gods may know. Before you can return to the land of the living, you must go to the land of the dead. Only the prophet Tiresias can tell you how to get home.

So Circe told me how to find my way to Hades, the land of the dead.

There I finally found Tiresias.

When you return to your home, it will be filled with men who are trying to steal your wife and your money. Don't tell anyone who you are. Dress yourself as a poor stranger, and Zeus will help you.

Then I returned to Circe. She gave us food and water for the long trip back, but she also gave me these warnings:

Be careful when you hear the songs of the Sirens! You will die if you listen to them for long.

Meanwhile, I have given you food. When you come to the island where the cattle of Apollo, the sun god, graze, do not harm them. If they are harmed, you will lose your ship and your men.

And so I sailed on, with only one ship and a handful of men.

We came at last to the island where Apollo's cattle grazed.

Circe has warned us. We must not harm any of the cattle.

But bad winds kept us from sailing on. A month passed. Our food began to run out.

Please let us kill and eat just one!

No! We must not harm the cattle! We can catch fish to eat.

But one day I awoke to a terrible sight.

You fools!

Finally the wind changed, and we went on. But soon the sun went away, and we sailed into a terrible storm.

Just as Circe had warned, my ship sank and my men drowned. I stayed alive by holding onto a piece of the boat.

After many days I came to Calypso's lonely island. Here I would find the years of sadness that Circe had told me about.

As the ship sailed toward Ithaca, Odysseus fell into a deep sleep.

The men sailed all that night. The morning star could be seen by the time they reached Odysseus' island.

Gently they carried the sleeping hero to a safe place. Then they quietly sailed away.

As Odysseus slept, the goddess Athena spread a fog over the land.

Yes, I will help you. But you must look more like the poor traveler you say that you are.

So Athena changed Odysseus to look like a poor old man.

Now, go to the hut of old Eumaeus, your swineherd. He is still faithful to you, though he fears that you will never return. Stay with him. I will send your son Telemachus to you.

So Odysseus walked to the hut of Eumaeus. But as he drew near, he was attacked by dogs.

Help! I'm just a poor old traveler!

Odysseus knew how to fool the dogs. He dropped his cane and lay on the ground as if he were dead. Then Eumaeus came and drove the dogs away.

Ah, good stranger, I welcome you!

Odysseus spent the day with Eumaeus. They ate together that evening.

It is good food and company that you have shared with me, friend.

Ah, it would be better, but hard times have come since my master went away.

45

Meanwhile, Odysseus' son Telemachus was coming home from his search for news of his father. Athena found him watching the storm.

When morning comes, do not return to your father's house! Go to the hut of old Eumaeus.

I will do as you say, Goddess.

When morning came, Telemachus went to see his father's swineherd.

Inside, Odysseus and Eumaeus had just finished their breakfast.

Good friend, someone is coming. It must be someone well known to you, for your dogs are wagging their tails.

Let Telemachus know your secret.

Then Athena changed Odysseus back to his real self.

But Telemachus stepped back in fear. Was this a man or was it a god who stood before him? So Odysseus came to him and spoke.

I am not a god. I am your father. Together we will sweep away this bad luck which has fallen on our home.

48

Now you must go home alone. You must tell no one who I am. Don't be afraid. I will come soon!

That evening, Odysseus went to the main house. He was again dressed as a wandering beggar.

Inside the great hall, the men were at their usual feast. Odysseus walked among them, begging for food. Some of the men gave him their scraps.

Here, old man, eat this.

The next day, there was an even greater feast than usual.

A toast! To Penelope—who will get a husband today!

Penelope went to the room where Odysseus' bow was kept.

Oh, Odysseus! Tears fill my eyes, but I have decided what to do.

Men of Ithaca! Whoever can string this bow and shoot an arrow through those twelve axes is the man whom I will marry!

So the contest began. Meanwhile, Penelope went to her room until the winner was known.

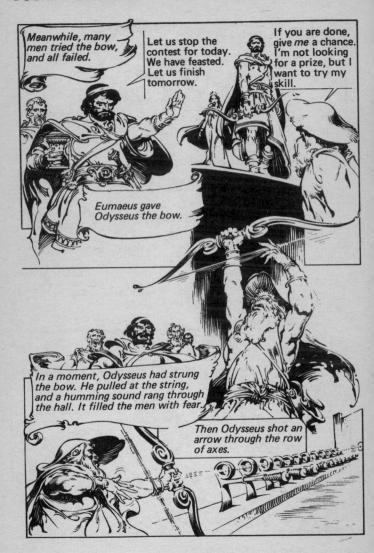

Meanwhile, many men tried the bow, and all failed.

Let us stop the contest for today. We have feasted. Let us finish tomorrow.

If you are done, give *me* a chance. I'm not looking for a prize, but I want to try my skill.

Eumaeus gave Odysseus the bow.

In a moment, Odysseus had strung the bow. He pulled at the string, and a humming sound rang through the hall. It filled the men with fear.

Then Odysseus shot an arrow through the row of axes.

In that way Odysseus took back his home.

Now this terrible deed is finished. Call the servants to carry out the bodies and clean the hall. Then happiness can return to this place.

I want you to burn sulfur. Its smoke will kill the poison that has lived in this house for so long.

Yes, we will do that. But you must get ready to meet your wife.

Odysseus sat in the place of honor. He longed to tell his wife that he was home.

Where is Penelope?

I will call her.

But first, there is one thing to be done. Eurycleia, take your maids and move our bed to its usual place.

At this, Odysseus jumped to his feet.

What? Our bed has been moved? How can it be?

At this, Penelope knew that the stranger was the same Odysseus she had married.

Dear Odysseus, do not be angry. For now I know it is truly you. We both know that no one could ever move our bed.

Long ago, Odysseus had built their bed using a strong olive tree. The tree had grown in the place where he built their bedroom. Only he and Penelope knew that the bed was rooted to the earth.

And so, twenty years had passed, but Odysseus had finally come home to rest in the arms of his wife. His travels were at last over.

THE END

COMPLETE LIST OF POCKET CLASSICS AVAILABLE

CLASSICS

C 1 Black Beauty
C 2 The Call of the Wild
C 3 Dr. Jekyll and Mr. Hyde
C 4 Dracula
C 5 Frankenstein
C 6 Huckleberry Finn
C 7 Moby Dick
C 8 The Red Badge of Courage
C 9 The Time Machine
C10 Tom Sawyer
C11 Treasure Island
C12 20,000 Leagues Under the Sea
C13 The Great Adventures of Sherlock Holmes
C14 Gulliver's Travels
C15 The Hunchback of Notre Dame
C16 The Invisible Man
C17 Journey to the Center of the Earth
C18 Kidnapped
C19 The Mysterious Island
C20 The Scarlet Letter
C21 The Story of My Life
C22 A Tale of Two Cities
C23 The Three Musketeers
C24 The War of the Worlds
C25 Around the World in Eighty Days
C26 Captains Courageous
C27 A Connecticut Yankee in King Arthur's Court
C28 The Hound of the Baskervilles
C29 The House of the Seven Gables
C30 Jane Eyre
C31 The Last of the Mohicans
C32 The Best of O. Henry
C33 The Best of Poe
C34 Two Years Before the Mast
C35 White Fang
C36 Wuthering Heights
C37 Ben Hur
C38 A Christmas Carol
C39 The Food of the Gods
C40 Ivanhoe
C41 The Man in the Iron Mask
C42 The Prince and the Pauper
C43 The Prisoner of Zenda
C44 The Return of the Native
C45 Robinson Crusoe
C46 The Scarlet Pimpernel

COMPLETE LIST OF POCKET CLASSICS AVAILABLE
(cont'd)

SHAKESPEARE